Simon Mayor

New Celtic Mandolin

New Celtic Mandolin
Simon Mayor

ISBN 0--9522776-2-X

First edition 1998

First published in 1998 by
Acoustics (Publishing)
PO Box 350
Reading RG6 7DQ
Berkshire
England

© Simon Mayor 1998

Layout and design of front and back cover by John Hedgecock
Edited by Hilary James and Andrew Baum
Illustrations © Hilary James 1998

Contents

Hello

Mention the words 'Celtic Music' to someone and the mandolin may not be the first thing that springs to mind, but it's an area that offers enormous possibilities and endless fascination for those of us hooked on the little instrument.

Many tunes, of course, are sufficiently simple that a mandolin rendition is going to pose no particular problem, but there are also those thought of specifically as 'fiddle tunes' or 'pipe tunes', which contain phrasings that at first may not sit comfortably on the mandolin. Well, it's always good to have a challenge, and I've not fought shy of including some of these, taking the opportunity to discuss how best to adapt them. At the same time, exploiting the strengths of the mandolin is always my main concern when making suggestions for decoration, and so on.

I've also gone further by including ideas that stretch mandolin technique beyond what is normally required for Celtic music: some of the chordal arrangements, the suggestions for trying tunes in 'weird' keys like E, and the tunes that venture out of first position. It's all designed to make you more familiar with the fingerboard and to improve all aspects of your playing.

So, this book is primarily about ideas for the mandolin and shouldn't be viewed as a source book for tunes; there are many good ones available. The pub session is also a great place for learning tunes, indeed it's an undeniable keystone of traditional music culture, but it can be a frustrating place for those of us trying to compete with fiddles, banjos and pipes (an awesome task for even the loudest mandolin). Subtlety tends to decrease with the consumption of alcohol! So, many arrangements, typically the slow airs, are for those who would expect the execution of every decorative trick to be heard and appreciated rather than drowned by beery chatter. The subtle approach, I hope.

I've used the word 'suggestions' a couple of times, and it's an important word; nothing in this book is meant to be prescriptive, it's against the very nature of traditional music. What you'll find in these pages is one person's ideas, one person's style, and while learning the arrangements exactly as written will, I hope, be both helpful and satisfying, so much the better if you absorb the ideas into your own musical identity. Unlike classical music, traditional music hasn't developed so rigid a set of rules as to how it should be played, the emphasis being more on the musician's own interpretation than on trying to reflect the composer's or the conductor's intentions. This diversity of approach is well reflected in the interviews in this book - extract what wisdom you will! There are stylistic boundaries of course, but ultimately it's down to you.

The tunes are presented in both standard music notation and tablature; the two are always vertically aligned so if you're using the tablature, keep half an eye on the music to see the rhythm. I'd echo my plea elsewhere in print to learn to read music if you can; while tablature is a wonderful tool it will never be an international language for musicians, and if you want to explore written music more widely, you need the ability to read the 'dots'.

I've generally used terms to describe decoration that are descriptive. The subject is discussed in context throughout the book, but here's an introductory guide.

A 'pull-off' is also called a 'cut'. Strike only the grace note with the plectrum then sound the full note by pulling the left hand finger sharply down off the string. I've differentiated between this and a 'push-off' - the same effect but with the finger flicking up rather than down.

A 'hammer-on' ('hammer') is the opposite of a pull. Strike the grace note then sound the full note by hammering down with the next left hand finger.

A slide up to a note is indicated by a short line, the word itself, and usually some left hand fingering marks. Occasionally I've suggested slides *down* to a note as well.

A grace note such as the low G at the start of this example, where no particular style of decoration is marked, is meant to be played just a split second before the main G of the melody: hit both the G and D strings with the plectrum.

A 'roll' is indicated either by grace notes or by the mordent expression mark in the first example here. It could be played as a simple hammer-on and pull-off figure. More often players would squash five notes into the same space in a hammer, pull, pull, hammer sequence. Only the first note is played with the plectrum, the others are sounded just with the left hand.

A decorative triplet involves turning one note (or two notes) into three of the same. Where to do it is a matter of personal style and preference, but the examples here show how a phrase could be played.

Incidentally, as in the standard notation, grace notes also appear in a slightly smaller face in the tablature. Fingerings and expression markings are not repeated; it's easy enough to glance above.

The Teetotaller's Fancy

trad arr. Mayor

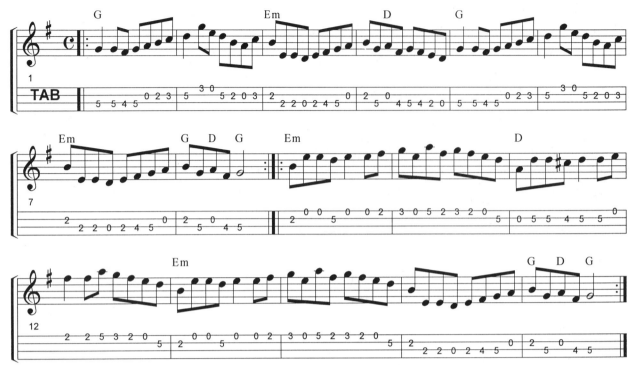

This reel is written out in two ways to show how a tune can come to life when it is decorated.

Above is the unadorned melody; it's fairly well known but if you're not familiar with it take a few moments to get acquainted. Opposite is the same tune with lots of 'fairy dust' on it. I've suggested a triplet run up to the first note; if we start this on a down stroke it means that the first note of the tune proper becomes an up stroke. It's generally a good idea to start bars (and in particular the first bar of a tune) with a down stroke, you get a better emphasis that way, but with practice a conscious strong upward flick of the wrist as you reach the G can provide an equally positive start.

In the next bar I've suggested a down stroke on both the first and second notes; it generally feels more natural to play each pair of quavers as down-up. Bar 5 contains a little variation on the original melody; we'll talk more later about how to vary melodies, but notice how the new phrase still sounds fine under the accompanying chords. In bar 6 I've dropped the first note by an octave; you can let this ring under the next couple of bars (it's a common trick).

A similar thing happens in bar 13, but I've also tied the next two notes to introduce a syncopated feel. At the start of bar 9 I've suggested a roll down from the B to the G; play the B and push-off before you play the G. The open A string sounds with the force of the first finger leaving the string rather than a separate pick stroke.

In bar 10, the start of the second section, play the D on the second string as you hit the open E, then slide your third finger up to the seventh fret to play the next note as two unison Es. This produces a discordant sound which immediately resolves to unison. I call it a 'choke' effect which is only easily available where open strings are involved, but I have seen some people with a particularly wide left hand stretch play chokes where both strings are fretted.

Bar 14 gives an opportunity to pull off from a grace note onto the second of the two open Es. The obvious thing is to come from an F♯ but there's no reason not to use a different note: I've suggested a B using your fourth finger. It's a bit trickier, but an unusual effect. The last three bars contain various pull-offs and push-offs. Notice the suggested pick directions in bar 15. Here, you're not pulling off a grace note, but a note that is actually part of the tune.

Mrs Murray of Abercarney

trad arr. Mayor

A tune from the Gow collection.

Mrs Murray of Abercarney is one of those tunes that can easily stay on your mind for days on end, so beware! Its 'hook', to use a pop music term, is the syncopation in the first couple of bars, which give way to the more flowing feel of bars 4 - 7. It's like a lot of American old-time music in having an insistant, almost hypnotic quality. Who knows, it could easily have evolved into a frailed banjo tune if it had ever crossed the Atlantic.

It's not particularly difficult to play; everything is in first position and I've suggested just a few places to ornament that feel comfortable on the mandolin. As it happens, these are all push-offs rather than pull-offs. Remember this involves plucking the string with the left hand finger as it flicks upwards off the fingerboard, causing the string to sound on the note below through the force of the release. A pull is the same thing but involves snapping the left hand finger *down* to release the string. Depending on the context of an ornament you may find it easier to push than to pull; the effect is the same. There are no hard and fast rules, it's simply a case of what feels easiest.

trad arr. Mayor

Lord Mayo

If you have a lower member of the mandolin family you may like to use it on this tune. It was worked out on a mandocello; the long sustain of the lower strings seems to suit the piece, particularly in places like the start of bar 6 where I've suggested a droning low G (or a C on a mandocello of course) under the entire bar. Play it freely and wistfully.

The Athol Highlanders

trad arr. Mayor

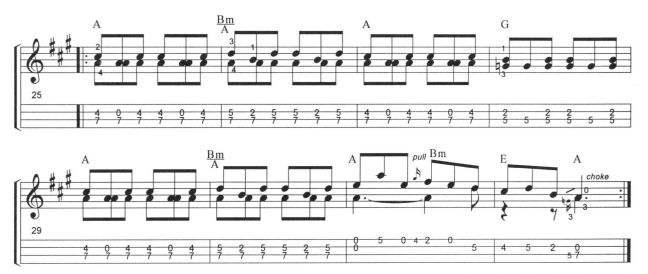

The Athol Highlanders is one of the most famous of all pipe tunes.

It poses some interesting challenges for the mandolin as I've tried to retain a pipe style drone for as much of the tune as I could. This involves holding down an A with your fourth finger on the third string while your other three fingers play the tune. It's not easy, particularly as most folk tunes are playable in first position and you can get away without using your little finger too much if you really want to be lazy! So give this a try, but remember, if your left hand starts to ache, stop immediately and rest it. Muscles respond best to frequent but gentle encouragement into unfamiliar positions.

In the second section (starting at bar 9), try to let each successive note of the rising triads ring on under the next.

In the third section (starting at bar 17) the left hand gets some welcome relief from having to hold the drone A. The interesting feature here is the pull-offs from a high C♯ to an A; give them lots of attack. Bars 20 and 24 have drone Es (top string open) above the melody. These notes are printed small as a warning not to play them too strongly lest they intrude.

The drone returns in the last section. I've suggested a grace note at the end of some sections which involves sliding from a G natural up to an A on the third string and hitting the second string simultaneously. I call this effect a 'choke' - a fleeting discord before the final note.

The Butterfly

trad arr. Mayor

This deservedly popular slip jig has a haunting quality. Don't be tempted to race it, as you'll lose all the beauty of the tune. The Butterfly is normally played in E minor, but the move up to A minor allows the melody to rock across three strings a lot of the time, supporting the sustain of the mandolin.

The first bar is typical: I've moved the notes of C and B onto the third string (use the third and fourth fingers of the left hand), leaving the open E and A strings to ring for the whole bar. This is important. Make sure your left hand doesn't inadvertently damp these strings otherwise the whole point of the arrangement is lost and you might as well play the phrase more easily in first position.

Bars 9 - 12 are essentially the same as bars 5 - 8, but as a variation some of the high A notes have been moved down an octave to the open second string; let them ring on under the whole bar.

The last four bars involve some very bunched chords in left hand fingering but follow the indications exactly as written and you shouldn't get tied in a knot.

Niel Gow's Lament for Abercarney

arr. Mayor

Another from Gow's collection. There are many different ways you could successfully finger this tune. I've moved it up to D from the original G for this arrangement, partly to take advantage of the singing quality of the top string, and also to bring out the thicker tone of the second and third strings higher up the neck when playing out of first position.

Notice the grace notes just before the F♯ in bar 3. This is an instance of where I would play all notes with a separate plectrum stroke rather than hammering-on and pulling-off; it creates a very different effect.

Dance of the Water Boatmen

Simon Mayor

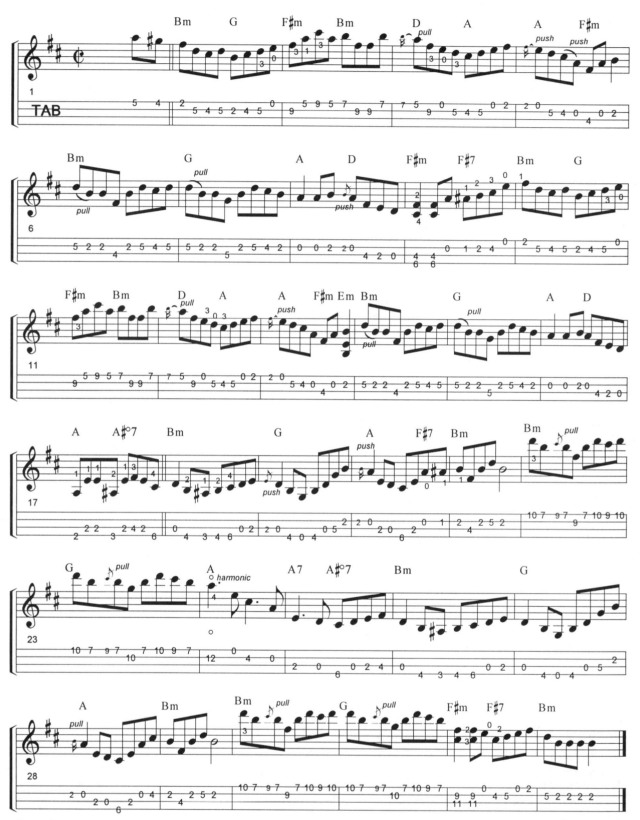

Unlike a traditional reel this contains some position changing, and is generally on the tricky side.

I like to use an open string as an aid to position changing; in a brisk tune like this it gives an extra split second to execute the change. Look, for example, at bar 2; as the last note is played on the open E string move your left hand up to third position and fret the F♯ on the ninth fret, second string. Play the next phrase up to the high C♯ then, in a similar way, descend to first position again in bar 4: the third finger plays the F♯, then play the open E string as the shift happens and the third finger is ready to play the D on the second string.

Bar 9 involves using what's known as 'half position'; the second finger moves back to play the B, the third finger the C♯.

In bar 24 play the A as a harmonic on the 12th fret second string; this gives you plenty of time to go back down to first position for the next phrase.

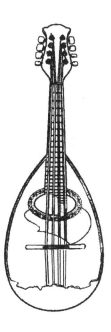

Waynesboro

trad arr. Mayor

This New England tune (probably of Irish derivation) works well with a gentle swingy feel.

The triplets are important, so try to play them crisply. I like to get the pick travelling down on the on-beat again as soon as possible after the triplet has thrown it out of sequence, so try the pick directions as marked to see if they work for you. The syncopations in bars 2 and 6 pose a similar problem, and once again I've indicated up strokes on the off-beats and downs on the on-beats. Once you're playing the triplets smoothly you can have some fun by shifting them to different beats in the bar. Here are alternatives for bars 1 and 3:

In bars 4 and 9, slide up to the C♯ - I prefer to use my second finger - and let it ring under the open E string. Then play the C♯ and slide to (but don't play) the B.

Such a Parcel of Rogues

trad arr. Mayor

Such a Parcel of Rogues is a hauntingly beautiful tune, as beautiful without harmony at all as with this chordal arrangement. There are copious fingering marks here to help with the left hand. Play it slowly but not too freely, leaving some sense of momentum.

The Wasp Reel

Simon Mayor

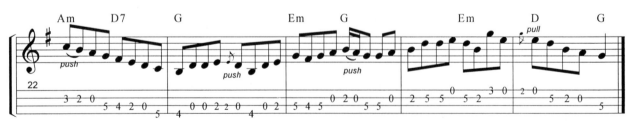

Simon Mayor

The Wasp Reel (in A)

We can be reasonably sure that most of the tunes in this book were not written with the mandolin in mind but the original tunes most decidedly were. The Wasp Reel started out life in the key of A but later seemed to fall under the fingers much more easily in G, so here are both versions - with a few subtle differences.

The G major version first: in bar 10 (and again in bar 14) notice the pick directions indicated. Because I've suggested a pull-off on the second quaver, start on a down-stroke again on the third. In bar13 and elsewhere 'choke' the top two strings to an E.

I've notated this tune exactly as I would play it, which doesn't mean I play it exactly like this every time of course, but you'll notice I use a *lot* of pulls and pushes; it really does make it come alive.

The Dark and Slender Boy

trad arr. Mayor

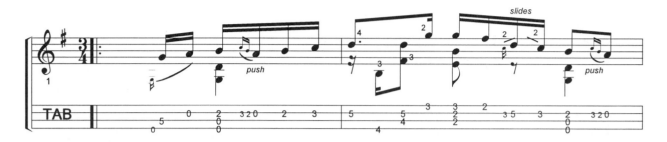

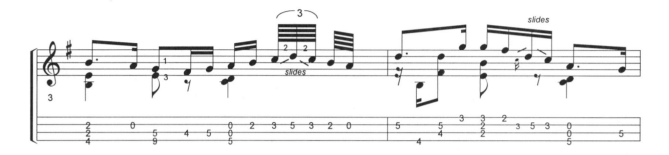

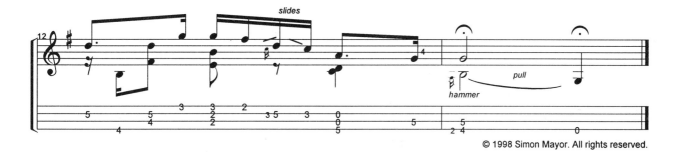

This fairly complex chordal arrangement was conceived for solo mandolin, but some very simple accompaniment may suit.

It's challenging to play this well: the main problem is to hold the left hand fingers down long enough on each note for the piece to have a sense of fluidity. Play the tune freely: it has a beautiful poignancy and you can allow yourself the luxury of treating the time signature and note values as the barest guide to what should be going on. It's a classic example of how neither standard notation nor tablature can successfully represent something from an aural tradition. But I've tried!

There are slides suggested in a lot of places. Most people find it fairly easy sliding up: pluck the first note, slide the finger and the second should ring through the residual energy in the string. Sliding down is a little harder as you're asking a short section of the string to ring that wasn't previously vibrating. It sounds difficult, but it does work provided that you retain the pressure on the string with the fingers of your left hand.

Up-and-down slides are even more difficult, and require considerable left hand pressure if they're going to work well. Take bar 2 as an example: fret the C with the second finger, then, as you pluck, give the left hand a quick flick up and down, the finger sliding up to the D and back to place. You'll find it much easier if all the joints on your left hand fingers are bent so the final knuckle falls perpendicularly onto the fingerboard. It's amazing how much strength you lose when executing little tricks like this if your fingers are falling onto the fingerboard at a shallower angle.

Bar 10 looks more difficult than it really is... I think... hopefully... maybe. Look carefully and you'll see the flourish is a simple scale of G major. Don't try picking every note; hit the open G string and then hammer on the A, B and C with fingers 1, 2 and 3. Do similarly on each string until you reach the top A with your third finger, then pluck and slide up to a B. The idea is to get it to sound smooth, so if it doesn't seem to be happening at first, slow right up and get your two hands co-ordinating properly. If you get really good at this you'll balance the force of the plucked and hammered notes so that you can't hear a difference. The effect of a fast flourish in the middle of a slow air can be very dramatic, particularly if it speeds a little as it heads for that top B.

Daley's Reel

trad arr. Mayor

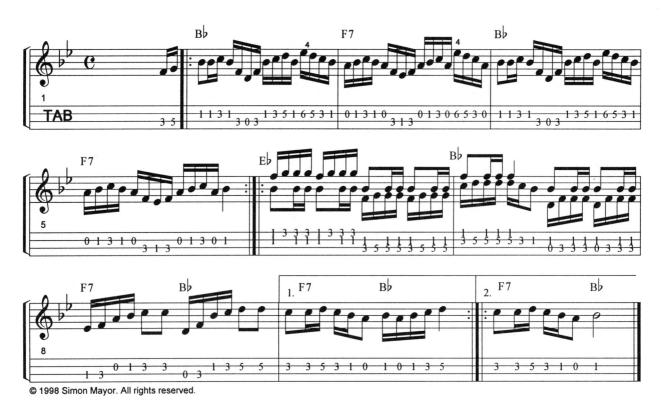

Bottom of the Punchbowl

trad arr. Mayor

The Gamekeeper's Reel

Simon Mayor

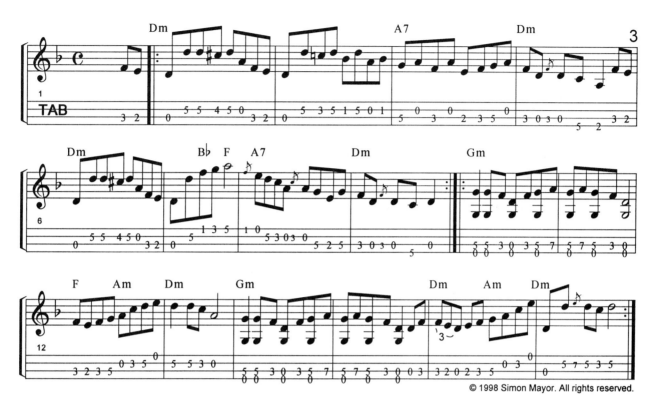

Solomon's Seal

Simon Mayor

The Steamboat Quickstep

trad arr. Mayor

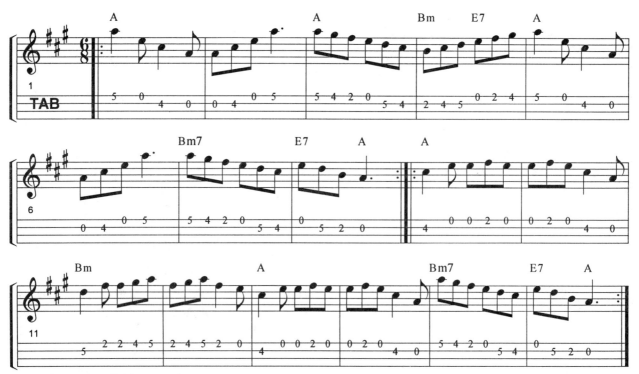

This is a really simple Scottish jig with a strong, insistent melody. I've not bothered suggesting any decoration as I'd like to play it (because of its simplicity) in other keys as a left hand exercise.

It's easy enough to spend your whole life playing traditional tunes just in G, D or A - the three common 'traditional' keys on stringed instruments. But it's tempting not to use the fourth finger in first position. Beware, it can sometimes go green and fall off through sheer neglect! This can be embarrassing, even messy. So, prevention being better than cure, try The Steamboat Quickstep in the different keys suggested opposite. The E♭ version has similar left hand shapes to the version above; if you were to put a capo on the first fret and play the A major pattern one string lower and without your first finger you'd get the same effect. But don't do that, just visualise it to help you know what your fingers *should* be doing.

Although the B♭ version could be played back on the top two strings with the same fingering as in E♭ , that's not the point of the exercise. So, starting with your second finger on the top B♭ , play the whole tune without changing position. Glance at the tablature if you're unsure.

The point of all this is twofold: first, it strengthens your little finger; second, it makes you better acquainted with the fingerboard; third, it shows how you can sometimes shift position if you want to decorate a specific note. In retrospect, the point of this is threefold. As an example of this last point, I've put a snap onto the very first note of the B♭ version which would have been impossible in first position, and very difficult even in the key of A, as you'd have had to use your little finger.

Steamboat Quickstep in E♭

Steamboat Quickstep in B♭

The Hopscotch Hornpipe

Simon Mayor

The Hopscotch Hornpipe goes up to third position and takes advantage of a tricky string crossing feature in bar 5. Look at the tablature for the suggested fingering to get the two top strings ringing against each other. The plectrum directions are important too, working a down-up-up, down-up-up pattern across the triplets. This is known as 'cross-picking' in bluegrass circles and is often done across three as well as two strings. It feels unnatural at first but is fast once it's become ingrained. Let the phrases in bars 12 and 13 ring across three strings. Triplets such as those in bar 16 can be played with three plectrum strokes or hammered and pulled.

Miss Brown's Favourite is a fast reel, and although played all in first position still involves great exercise for your little finger. Again, the fingering marked is important. I'd recommend an interesting trick for the last four quavers of bar 9. Don't move the tip of your second finger from the C to the G but pull it flat against the top string so that you fret the note with the ball rather than the tip of the same finger. Straighten up the finger again immediately and the C will have remained fretted for the whole phrase.

Johnnie Cope

trad arr. Mayor

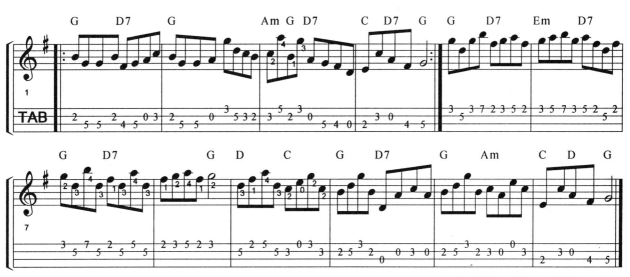

Miss Brown's Favourite

trad arr. Mayor

Farewell to the Shore

trad arr. Mayor

This very pretty Welsh waltz works well on the mandolin. The first eight and last eight bars have an identical melody but I've put in some different fingerings which vary the tone colour; you can mix and match them at will.

Bars 1 and 2 have a drone A beneath the tune - play this with your fourth finger on the third string. It's a bit of a stretch but the effect is worth it. Avoid catching the second or first string with this finger by making sure you bend every knuckle over into a tight arch. This is a good habit to cultivate in any case.

28

In bars 3 and 4 I've moved the left hand high up the neck in order to spread the notes out across the strings (check the tablature). In bars 7 and 8 I've used the open A string as a drone *above* the melody for a change; try to play this a little less prominently than the melody below, almost as if you're catching the A string by accident.

My preference is to play the second section (bars 9 - 16) entirely on the E string, maybe using tremolo on bars 9, 10 and 11. Staying on one string is definitely easier than string crossing for tremolo, but it's more likely to involve the left hand in some position shifts. The fingering I've shown works efficiently, and you might find it nice to make an audible shift with the second finger in bar 11 - in other words, slide your finger as you move.

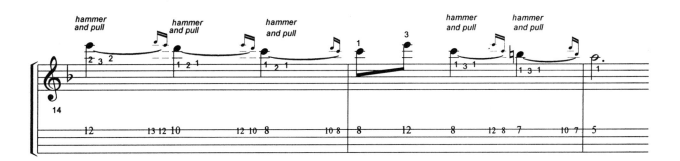

By the time you hit the top E in bar 12 you're on your fourth finger; try playing the note as a harmonic and then moving the same finger over to the second string to catch the A harmonic. Next another shift moving the second finger up to the F - it's not a fast tune so you've got lots of time.

Above, I've written out a detailed account of what you could do in bars 14, 15 and 16. It's a good way of getting the left hand back down to third position.

Play only the first note of each hammer and pull-off figure, that is the actual note of the melody. The grace notes, coming unusually *after* the beat, should sound only by the left hand hammering-on and pulling-off.

An alternative is to play bars 9 - 16 entirely with tremolo, in which case stay on the first string for the A harmonic (use your first finger).

The last eight bars contain some alternative fingerings to the first eight, but nothing too difficult. The very last note involves sliding up to the D (7th fret on the fourth string) while simultaneously playing the open D, the 'choke' effect of discord resolving to unison.

Huish The Cat

trad arr. Mayor

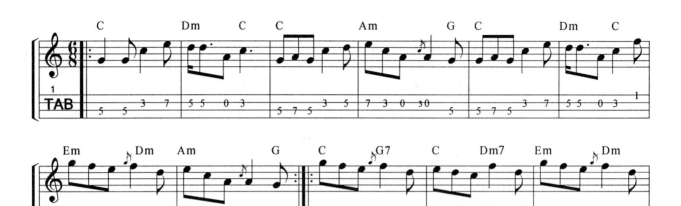

Bryan O'Lynn

trad arr. Mayor

Geese In The Bog

trad arr. Mayor

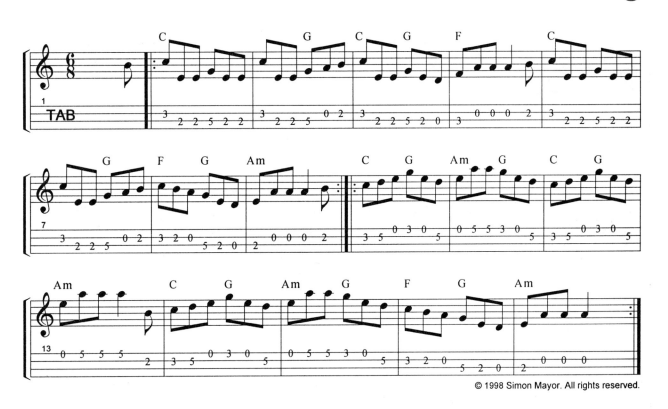

The Medlar Bush

Simon Mayor

John Stephen of Chance Inn

trad arr. Simon Mayor

This is a little heard but beautiful Scottish tune that lends itself to some rich harmonies. I've always thought the English language didn't contain enough suitable adjectives to describe music, but one friend thought this tune was "warm and cosy"! It's one of those tunes that seems to work well at any tempo: brisk, steady or even as a slow air. It's up to you how you play it, but the arrangement as printed was conceived as a slow air for solo mandolin, and probably wouldn't be too easy if you tried to take it too fast.

The left hand fingering is all-important if you are going to execute it well; the only real advice is to follow the markings and you shouldn't go too far wrong. Don't be tempted to play it too quickly; once you've got the left hand moving smoothly try to give it just a gentle bounce. Watch the rhythm closely for the 'Scots snaps', the semiquaver/dotted quaver figures found, for example, in the last beat of bar 1.

Because the fingering is bunched in a lot of places you may prefer to try this on a mandola or even mandocello if you have one. The warm tones of the mandolin's larger relatives would suit well.

Little Molly-O

trad arr. Mayor

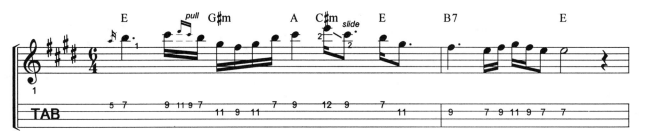

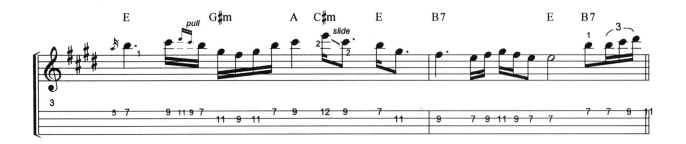

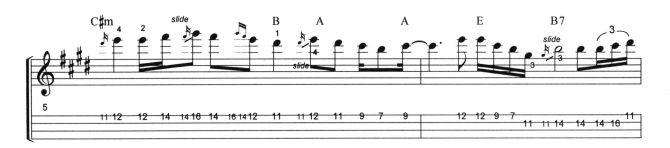

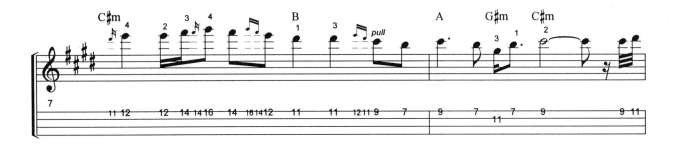

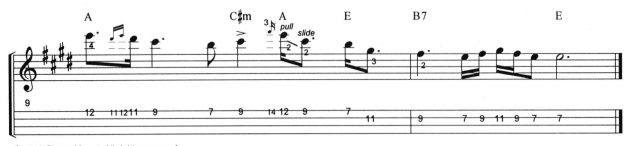

A beautiful slow air.

I recorded it in the key of E major, unusual for traditional tunes, but in the context of a CD it gave some subliminal relief from D, G and A. Although I played the tune in a lower octave as well, it gave me a chance to play high up the neck in closed position. This means, quite simply, that no open notes are used. For most folk tunes, you can get by without learning how to do this, as an 'open-stringiness' is really part and parcel of the style, but it's a very necessary skill if you want to play other sorts of music, and even some Celtic-related forms like bluegrass rely heavily on closed position playing.

Its advantage is very simple: a fingering pattern learned in closed position can be played in any key simply by moving the starting point to another place on the neck. And because the mandolin (unlike a guitar) is a symetrically tuned instrument - in other words all the strings are a fifth apart - it makes it a little easier.

So, when you're thoroughly familiar with this, try using the same fingering pattern but starting with your first finger on the 4th fret top string instead of the 7th. You'll be playing in C♯ major with no more difficulty; sounds impressive when you think that's seven sharps!

A position change is necessary in order to get the high notes. If you look at the left hand fingering in bar 5, I've advised keeping fourth position up to the first note, then switching from the fourth to the second finger on the high E. This gives you just enough fingers to hit the top G♯. Later in the bar the left hand moves back to fourth position - watch the fingering. It's often a good idea to manœvre position changes onto long notes if you can. They usually sound smoother, if not undetectable.

Straying from the tune...

Soldier's Joy (version 1)

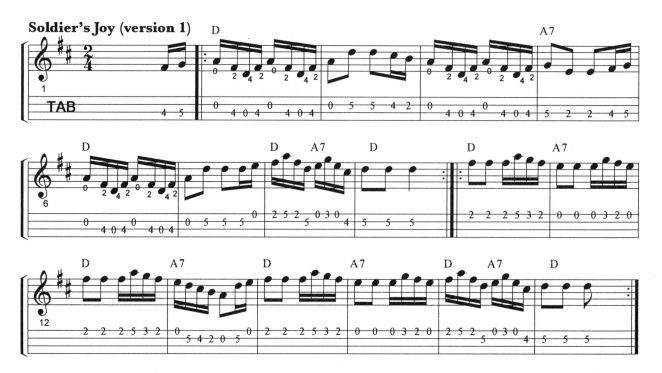

Folk tunes didn't start life on a piece of paper but by someone picking up an instrument and twiddling around until something good came out. The danger of writing them down - and yes, that includes what I'm doing in this book(!) - is that people may see the notated versions as in some way 'correct'. Of course the ability to read music is a huge asset, but the very fact that most traditional tunes exist in many different versions means they have been passed down courtesy of some people's patchy memories.

Soldier's Joy (version 2)

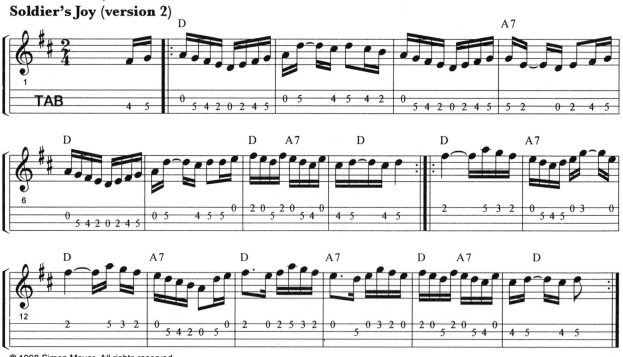

Remember too that, unlike in the classical world, many folk musicians write tunes as well, and they're as inclined to twiddle around with someone else's masterpiece as they are with their own. Litigation is not a traditional issue!

So if you want to modify a tune in a unique way how do you start? On a subtle level, the way a tune is decorated is individual to each and every player. Even if you spend a long time learning every slide and pull-off in these pages, believe me you'll be doing it your own way within an hour of putting the book down. Variations in tunes are more noticable when chunks of the melody change. Compare the two versions of Soldier's Joy on the oposite page: the first is from East of the Atlantic, the second from the West.

The two versions are noticably the same tune, but where the first relies on arpeggio figures to catch the ear, these are turned into linear figures in the second, with the syncopation in bars 3, 5, 7 etc. giving it a decidedly American flavour.

Incidentally, try playing the broken chords in the first version across three strings as I've indicated in the fingering. It's a little harder work for the left hand but gets the mandolin ringing nicely.

So, back to improvising around a melody. Whistle or hum the tune to yourself and strum the chords (D and A7 as shown) on the mandolin, then do it with the book closed. I've chosen Soldier's Joy for this because it's a really well known tune and the straightforward way to accompany it is with just these two chords. If you can feel these chord changes coming you're already half way there.

Now let's think of something very basic we can do over this same chord sequence instead of playing the tune. We can play arpeggios. After all, they're a feature of the first version at least. But because we're improvising, we'll halve the note values to give ourselves time to think. Here's what it might sound like:

Example 1

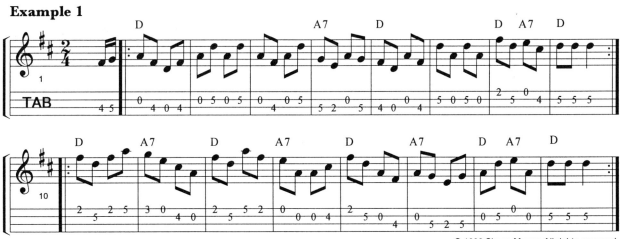

Over every D chord we're using the notes making up that chord: D, F♯ and A. Over every A7 chord we're doing likewise with the notes A, C♯, E and G (the flattened seventh). Once you can hear the chord changes, this is a sure way of playing something that fits. If what you came up with is anything like the above it may not be too exciting, but at least it will be original - it will have something of you in it.

We can make things more interesting by adding passing notes (notes in between those already there). Have a look at the example below now; all the notes in the first example are still in place but many have had their values halved to make room for the passing notes. These new notes needn't be part of the accompanying chord to work.

Example 2

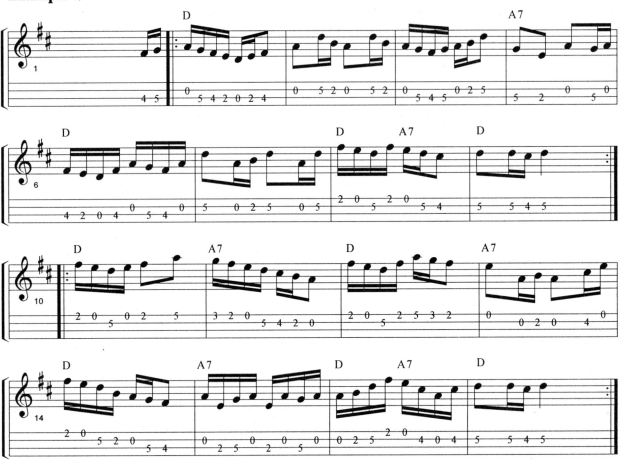

Now the variation begins to sound more interesting, more musical. The passing notes give more of the rhythmic feel of the original, while the overall shape remains similar - it rises and falls in more or less the same places. Because the first of each semiquaver pair is contained in the accompanying chord, the variation is 'anchored' harmonically.

trad arr. Mayor

St Anne's Reel

'West'

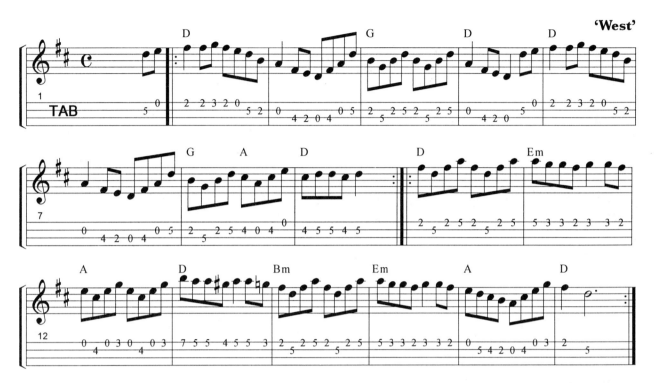

Here are two versions of St Anne's Reel which I've labelled 'West' and 'East', being loosely representative of what you might find either side of the Atlantic.

In bar 2 of 'East' try to let the open A string ring over the F♯ and D. Aim for a similar effect in bar 3 by playing the B and E with the ball of the first finger of the left hand. In bar 13 (of either version) go for the high B with your little finger rather than change position.

'East'

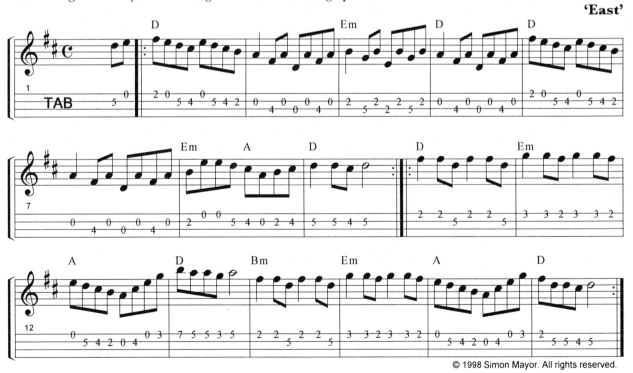

St Anne's Reel - variations

trad arr. Mayor

Variation 1

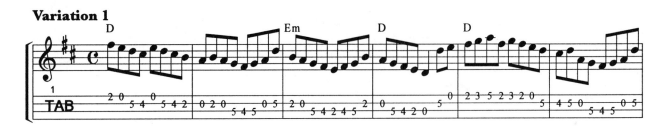

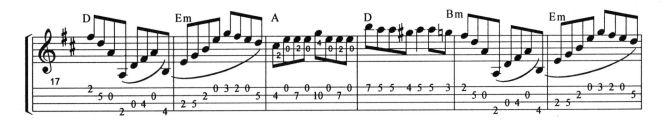

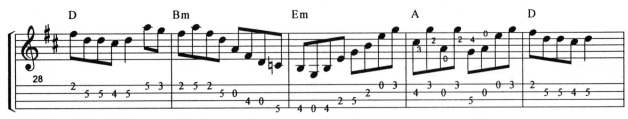

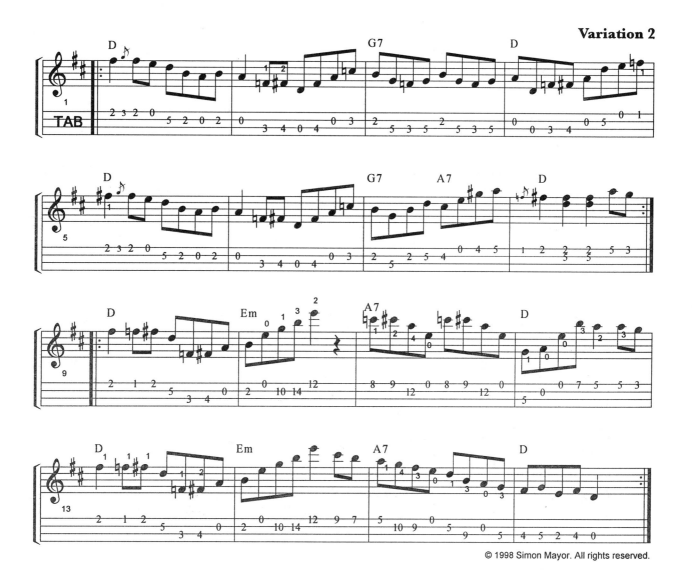

Here are two suggestions for variations on St Anne's Reel - I can't really call them improvisations as I've thought them out in advance, but they're the sort of thing experienced players might rattle off.

Variation 1 is diatonic, in other words for the most part it doesn't stray from the notes of the host key, D major. There's a venture into third position at the start of bar 9. The first finger moves to the D on the second string for the third note of the bar, using the preceding open E as a chance to change position. Note also how the last three notes of bar 10 cross strings to get a bell-like cascade at the end of the phrase. A similar effect happens with the open Es in bar 11. Watch the fingering in bar 19: the open Es are used to the full.

Variation 2 is more in an American style, with a bluesy, bluegrassy feel. Much use is made of chromatic passing notes (the last note of bar 4 for example), the flattened third of the scale and the flattened seventh. These are all techniques you can use to shape your own breaks.

Carolan's Frolics

O'Carolan arr. Simon Mayor

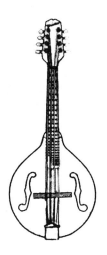

43

Dérobée de Guingamp

Breton trad arr. Mayor

45

❧ 46 ❧

Eliz Iza

Breton trad arr. Simon Mayor

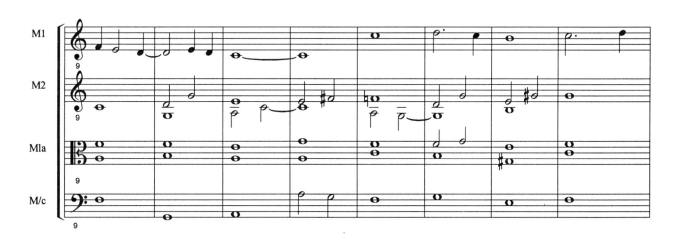

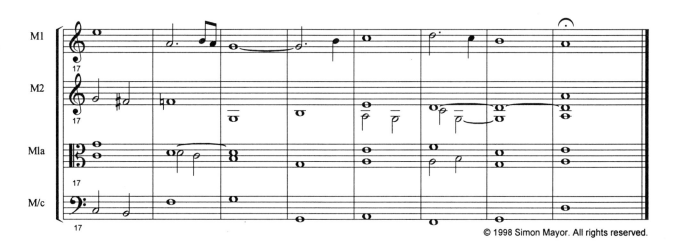

Interviews

I make reference elsewhere in these pages to the importance of playing with others as the best and most enjoyable way of learning. It follows that if you can't actually sit down and play with somebody, soliciting a few opinions during the course of an interview is the next best thing, and it gave me the excuse to contact five players whose styles I certainly admire. I'm grateful to them all for being generous with their wisdom.

Intriguingly, you'll find no real consensus of opinion on a lot of the subjects covered, so here are a few notes on subjects that crop up:

Types of mandolin

Round-backs are the traditional Italian design, used almost exclusively by classical mandolinists. Good ones can project really well, but there are many around made just for the Italian tourist trade. The tone is considered by most to be overly bright and lacking in 'oomph' for Celtic music.

Gibsons and Gibson-style mandolins take inspiration from violin design incorporating a shallow body and a carved back and table. They can have either an oval sound-hole, or two f-holes. The shape can be either a simple tear-drop, or sport decorative scrolls and points. Cheap copies will be made from plywood, steamed and pressed into an arch. Many excellent modern luthiers throughout the world have refined this design. It was originally developed for the classical orchestras of the 20s and 30s but is now popular in all musical idioms.

Cittern-style mandolins. These were developed by Stefan Sobell and other luthiers in Britain and Ireland specifically with Celtic music in mind, and are intended as much for an accompanying role as for tune playing. Stefan told me his inspiration was a combination of baroque plucked instruments, an old Portuguese guitarra, and a 1930s Martin arch-top guitar. The instruments have flat backs but carved tops, oval holes, and deep bodies. Stefan describes their sound as "less homogenous than a Gibson-style, softer on the bass and more 'clangy' in the treble".

Flat mandolins. By this I mean totally flat, with no carving on either the front or the back. This is generally a cheaper option for makers, although some of the more shallow bodied ones can sound surprisingly good.

Thomastik Strings. The vast majority of players use round-wound strings, but Brian Taheny states a preference for Thomastiks. These are basically flat-wound violin strings, which produce a 'woodier', less zingy sound than round-wounds. They're expensive but last a long time because dirt can't get trapped in the windings. You'll love them or hate them.

Rather than print contact information which may become out of date, the author is happy to supply addresses of luthiers, string manufacturers, and artists' representation if contacted via the publisher's address on page 67. Information may also be gleaned from the Acoustics website.

The Andy Irvine Interview

One of the most respected of all Irish artists, Andy Irvine played a seminal role in the dramatic changes in approach to Irish traditional music that were taking place in the late 60s and early 70s. His mandolin style owed little to the 'hack out the tune behind the singer' attitude that had prevailed; it was characterised by mesmerising counter-melodies often played in conjunction with other mandolin family players, notably Johnny Moynihan, Paul Brady and Donal Lunny. Complex, but never intrusive, his playing has graced a succession of leading Irish bands over the years. The number of players around today whose style bears Irvine hallmarks is testimony to his continuing influence.

What's your musical background? Have you always played the mandolin?

I started at the age of 13 playing a guitar. I asked my parents to give me a 'cello for my 13th birthday but unfortunately there has never been such a thing as a cheap 'cello and so they bought me a cheap guitar - so cheap, in fact that my first teacher wouldn't take me until I had something better. Fortunately, the Tatay Spanish guitar was within my parents affordability! I knew I was interested in music from an early age but could not find the music.

My mother had been a musical comedy actress and I had all these old chipped, cracked 78s, which I used to listen to in the absence of anything better. I found classical music, which I was studying on guitar, to be reasonably interesting but very hard work. Ultimately, when I told my teacher that I was having difficulty with the Bach Courante I was supposed to be playing, he advised even longer hours of practice. I thought "to hell with this, nice and all as Bach is, there must be something else". Within a short time, I heard Lonnie Donnegan and attached my colours immediately to the

Skiffle mast - not difficult for a budding Segovia!

I graduated through Lonnie - and I should impress upon you that I'm talking about his first two EPs 'Backstairs Session' and 'Skiffle Session'; by the time he made the LP I was an ex-Donegan fan - and through him, discovered Woody [Guthrie], who was and still is my biggest hero. I was doing a pretty passable impression of Woody.

Jack Elliot, after singing a song with me for the first time in 1959, said in amazement "Gee Andy, you sound more like Woody than I do!" When I discovered other people in Dublin who were interested in such matters I quickly gave up being an actor for the idealistic life of a man following the usually unpaid, or badly paid, life of a folk-singer, around 1964.

What attracted you to the mandolin - after all, it's not such a common instrument in Irish music as it is in, say, bluegrass?

My attraction to the mandolin had started in about 1958 or 59 when I realised that Woody played it. Basically I just wanted to be Woody, so I bought a flat-ish

backed mandolin in a shop in Notting Hill Gate, the name of which I can almost remember, but not quite. I think Jack was with me because he was living in that area in '58 and '59. I quickly discovered that playing 'More Pretty Girls Than One' without Cisco Houston sounded a bit bare.

The next discovery was music closer to home. In Dublin we were heavily into Ewan McColl, Peggy Seeger and Bert Lloyd and those Radio Ballad programmes like 'Singing the Fishing'. Irish music in Dublin was restricted to The Clancys. Though we liked the songs, we found the presentation far too 'strokey' for our idealistic attitudes. In the country it was different. We soon became people who travelled a lot in order to be in the same space and listen to the music of such as Willie Clancy. By this time I was playing mandolin with Johnny Moynihan and eventually with him in a band called Sweeney's Men.

Were there any specific players, not necessarily mandolinists, who inspired you when you were starting?

Apart from Woody and Johnny I never consciously was motivated by any other mandolin player.

I remember seeing you with Planxty in the early 1970s with the original line up: Donal Lunny, Christy Moore, Liam O'Flynn and you. I was knocked out by the whole concert, but what made a particular impression on me was the way you interacted with Donal Lunny. Irish players I'd managed to see before that seemed to 'accompany' songs by just playing the tune in unison with the singer, yet here you were weaving all sorts of counter melodies behind Christy Moore's vocals. How did the style come about? Did you just busk it all or did you spend hours with Donal working out every last note?

In Sweeney's Men, Johnny and myself had discovered that the bouzouki, which he was playing by then, and the mandolin had a really nice feel when used together in harmony and contrapuntalness. We explored this to some extent in 'Rattlin Roarin Willie' for example but I think it was developed more highly by myself and Donal Lunny in the early days of Planxty. From the beginning we had a really good musical relationship. I remember early rehearsals for 'Raggle Taggle Gypsies' where we were filled with joy by the sounds we were making together. In those early days of Planxty there was a free spirit and we fitted in with each other without too much thought. The music was somehow new and we made discoveries at every turn.

By the time of the second go round of Planxty in 1979, we were all a little more clued in and some of the things we did at that time stand out in my mind as the best collaborations I was ever involved in. The interplay on things like 'Little Musgrave', where there was room for extemporisation and 'True Love Knows No Season' and especially 'The Pursuit of Farmer Michael Hayes' are among the best music I was ever involved in.

All good things in bands are outside the control of any one member and soon I found myself playing more and more as a soloist. Well, basically I had always been a soloist and far from it being a downer, I soon began to enjoy it more and more.

It seems to me that many Irish mandolin players are really banjo players who have simply transferred their technique across and have a very hard, attacking style. Your playing is much more lyrical. Were you consciously trying to get away from being banjoistic?

I was never interested in playing the 4 string banjo. Apart from being a lead instrument in jigs and reels, it had no attraction as a song accompanying instrument.

What qualities do you look for in a mandolin? I seem to remember you playing Gibson A models earlier in your career. Do you still use them or have you switched to something else?

When I was young, I was mad keen to own a Gibson mandolin. The first one I ever saw was played by Jimmy McGregor. I travelled Eastern Europe with a Gibson A3, the nicest mandolin I ever remember. Johnny Moynihan gave it to me and I left it on buses in Sofia, in lifts in Ljublana and in a tent in Bucharest, Romania. All those years I was travelling I never lost it until it was stolen out of a car in Paris in 1979. I still expect to see it again, though I'm not quite sure what I'll do when I do see it. Probably just look ruefully… since

then I have been very happy to have most of my instruments made by Stefan Sobell of Hexham, Northumberland. A fine instrument maker and a very genuine man.

Do you set the mandolin up in any particular way for the style you play? I've never played your mandolin but I heard you use a non-standard tuning?

Since quite early in my career I have tuned the mandolin to GDAD, as I do the guitar-bodied Irish derivation of the Greek bouzouki. I started off playing the mandolin as an accompanying instrument because it had more subtlety than the guitar tuned in Spanish tuning, which was all we knew at the time. Johnny Moynihan had developed the mandolin as a self-accompanying instrument as well, and I think we both made a big impression on each other. At one point he had taken off the double strings. I never did do that but I agreed with his tuning of GDAD. We were both a bit motivated by Old Timey music and knew this tuning from Appalachian fiddle tunes. We also liked the open top D string because it had resonances of the 5 string banjo.

The Maartin Allcock Interview

After a formal training on double bass, there are now few stringed instruments on which Maartin Allcock doesn't excel. The double bass makes but rare public appearances these days, as his skill on the mandolin and its lower pitched family members has led to a sparkling career in folk rock with long spells in Fairport Convention and Jethro Tull. Of the many aspects of his talent, it's perhaps his intuitive sense of harmony that is spoken of in the most revered tones by those who have worked with him....

You trained on double bass, but you're rarely seen with one these days. What attracted you to the mandolin?

Well I started on bass guitar and guitar round about the same time, about eleven or twelve. I decided at the age of six that I was going to be a musician after watching the Beatles on TV. There was a teacher at school, Doctor Ilic, who was allegedly the Serbo-Croat foreign minister in exile, and he did actually teach seven or eight languages. He used to disappear regularly and the rumour was that he'd gone into hiding from the KGB. Anyway, one of these times there was an opening on his instrument, the double bass, so I had a go. I'd briefly attempted the trombone but found it too cumbersome. The double bass fitted the bill perfectly, so for the next 5 or 6 years the most common comment I heard was, "That's a big violin", which is actually quite funny the first million times. I got quite good at travelling on public transport with it, although the London tube presented some problems I hadn't encountered before. Anyway, my school chum Dave Gleeson, who's now an artist, and I used to go to gigs together and his father had an old round-back mandolin which was never played, so I borrowed it for a year or so. About this time I was getting into Lindisfarne and Fairport Convention, two good-time bands who featured the mandolin. I think the first thing I played on the mando was 'Lady Eleanor'. I couldn't believe how easy it was. By this time I was also very serious about the bass guitar, while playing double bass in the Lancashire Schools Symphony Orchestra, with which I toured Denmark and Sweden as a teenager. So I got interested more in Dave Pegg, who played bass and mandolin in Fairport, who in one interview with Guitar magazine said that playing the mando helped his speed on the bass. I then started practising Bach on the mandolin, something I still do nowadays, because there's so much of it, and every part in one of his orchestral scores has a great tune to play. When I left school I went to Huddersfield Polytechnic School of Music, one of the best music schools in England at the time, where I studied double bass under Peter Leah, the principal bass player with the Hallé Orchestra for 25 years. He told me that I would never get into an orchestra as my fingering is wrong due to a childhood injury, so I left and went pro, playing in Mecca dance bands.

Just recently I've been playing electric mandolin with Banbury based band Freeway Jam but I do get to play double bass from time to time, and have used it on many albums. In fact last year I was asked to deputise for 'Sir' Danny Thompson, the ace bass guru. That was a thrill and an honour.

I know your've collected a lot of instruments over the years. Have you found an ideal mandolin yet or are you on a constant search?

The nearest I've got is my old Gibsons. I have two A2s, one from 1919 and one from

1921. The machine heads are not great, but they are very hard to find replacements for, for some reason. I quite like Peggy's [Dave Pegg's] F-shape Vanden, but I do prefer the teardrop shaped body with the oval sound-hole. They can really bark, so you have a fantastic dynamic range. I find that the F-shape mandos have a bit too much wood in them, although they look fantastic. When I first joined Fairport Convention I had a Suzuki flat-back with two horns, red-to-yellow sunburst. But one of the advantages of the mandolin, its portability, is also one of its weaknesses in that it's very nickable, and the Suzuki walked after my second Fairport gig, in Devon. Peggy gave me one of his top-of-the-range Ibanez F-shape mandolins as a consolation, which I can plug in and it's really a very nice instrument. I also have a Rob Armstrong guitar-shaped flat-back mandolin which sounds remarkably like a round-back, but as that's quite a specialised sound it doesn't get out as much as the others.

I'm not the only person to remark that you have a really relaxed posture when you're playing. Is this something you've consciously thought about? I'm asking because I know the double bass is notorious for giving people back problems and wondered if you'd had any posture advice at college.

I've been playing for so long that I've probably got better posture when I'm playing than when I'm not. I've never consciously

thought about it, except when I've got the Les Paul on, or my electric 12-string which weighs a ton. I just feel comfortable with the instrument and we bond. In fact when I get a new instrument we sleep together the first night. My wife is very understanding...

Have you done much experimentation with your string and plectrum gauges?

I use D'Addario J74 phosphor bronze strings because they are the best that I've found, and they sound great. It's much easier to get mandolin strings these days compared to when I was a lad, but still there are some strings out there which are not really that great. The gauges I use are: .011", .015", .026"w, and .040"w. This is the set that David Grisman endorses, so they must be OK. On the bouzouki I use D'Addario custom gauges: .012", .018" (nickel round-wound), .028" and .042" (both phosphor bronze wound). The nickel wound second strings give it more of a plain string kind of sound (obviously a pair of .018" plains would be horrible). On the mandocello I use D'Addario phosphor bronze custom gauges: .074", .048", .034", and .022". I use Jim Dunlop Tortex picks, the orange ones, .66mm, as they last forever (although on a particularly spirited thrashing session do wear down quite a bit). They also have a very good memory, I mean they mould themselves to your grip, so they are very comfortable. I've been using these since they came onto the market and use them for guitar, all the mandos, bouzouki, etc. There is also a very floppy pick which I use in the studio if I'm doing like a strummy rhythm part, and that's a Jim Dunlop nylon .46mm.

Have you been interested in Celtic music all your life, or was there an 'awakening' - like when you met Fergus Feely and joined The Bully Wee Band?

I was brought up in North Manchester and back a few generations my people were from Dundalk in Ireland. So we were brought up Catholic and the social thing involved quite a lot of Irish people. My brother used to win medals for Irish dancing. I went along a few times but was much more interested in the music. The first tune I remember is 'The Rakes Of Mallow' which I must have learned when I was about four or five. At school I found great excitement in Led Zeppelin, Deep Purple, The Who, and so on, and forgot about Irish music for a while, although I used to go and watch people like Planxty supporting Steeleye Span, who along with Fairport, were broadening the appeal of traditional music. I got serious about the bass guitar and did a lot of wood-shedding (practising technique for technique's sake) which was a common fault in the mid '70s. A few years later when I was asked to join the The Celtic folk band Bully Wee, I was picked up at the railway station in London by Fergus Feely, the octave mandola player. He asked me to play him my favourite tape, so I put on 'Joe Frazier' by Bruford, a *big* bass feature. At the end Fergus said, "I never feel like that", and played me some of the new Planxty album which just blew me away. Then I toured a lot in Ireland with Kieran Halpin, who, although a contemporary artist himself, showed me the joy of the Irish seisún and my liver has never been the same since.

You've played for many years in folk rock bands - notably Fairport Convention - but I know you managed to sneak a couple of Irish tunes into the Jethro Tull set on one tour. How did you go about amplifying a mandolin in fairly heavy surroundings? Did you feel you achieved a good 'acoustic' sound at any time, or were you aiming for a usable sound that wasn't necessarily faithful to the acoustic sound of the mandolin?

When I was asked to join Jethro Tull as a multi-instrumentalist, I took a whole van full of instruments with me, including a Stefan Sobell 10 string cittern, which I played on a track, 'Part Of The Machine', on the 20th Anniversary boxed set. On the live gig, I played keys, electric, acoustic and MIDI guitars, electric bouzouki and mandolin. I used the Ibanez which Peggy had given me. It had been out with Tull before and was no problem. It has one of the old Barcus Berry pickups installed and just goes straight into a DI box and sounds the same every night. I think it sounds very convincing. You can never get the same sound as pushing air into a microphone, but obviously at stadium gig levels that's impossible and standing tied to a

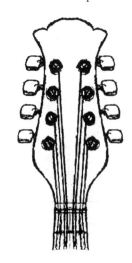

mic stand really cuts down the shapes you can throw.

I know you're fond of playing the lower instruments in the mandolin family, particularly the mandocello and your bouzouki-guitar hybrid. Does this stem from your background as a double bassist, or is it just something in your bones?

I suppose it does come from being a bass player, but then I was attracted to that because of the low notes. I think the bass is the foundation of all music and that it must trigger some primal frequencies inherent in the body. Also I like to play instruments that aren't very common, as there're more employment opportunities! The mandolin, although not exactly common-as-muck, is seen quite a bit more than the lower instruments but these bigger sisters balance beautifully with the mandolin, in the same way that a 'cello balances a string quartet.

Tell us about these lower instruments you've got.

The mandocello is made by Ovation from Connecticut. They started making them in 1994 and have made about a thousand of them. Mine is called a MC868-4, the -4 denoting that it's a natural finish. The back is moulded from a composite material of fibreglass and resin, the top is solid spruce, the neck is a 5 piece construction of mahogany and rock maple and the fingerboard is ebony. It's the same body and neck as their Elite guitar model and has the epaulettes of exotic woods around the many small sound-holes. It has a single cutaway and quite a slim body, unlike myself. It also features the Ovation Optima pre-amp which has a three band EQ, a notch filter, a bypass switch and a choice of either jack or balanced XLR outputs from the instrument. It also has a tuner built into the pre-amp panel on the side of the instrument and is altogether a space-age take on an old and not so loved instrument. I have three electric bouzoukis, two made by Rob Armstrong (one as half of a twin-neck with a Strat neck), and one by Andy Viccars which is a copy of my 1968 Gibson Goldtop Les Paul. I have a Stefan

Sobell bouzar, which is a bouzouki with a guitar body. This is a real Maserati. I have two Rob Armstrong fretless bass guitars, one electric and much recorded (including Beverley Craven's 'Promise Me') and one acoustic.

I know Sobell instruments are very popular among Celtic musicians, but surely they give a very different sound from the Ovation? Stefan's instruments are typically played quite loosely strung to get that 'slappy' sound, whereas having played it I know the strings on your Ovation are designed to sort the men out from the boys. Do you see them as doing very different jobs?

The two instruments definitely play different roles. The mandocello is a bass instrument in the same way that the violoncello is a bass instrument. The bouzar is more of a melodic/rhythmic instrument. When I first saw the Ovation mandocello I was in Mandolin Brothers, an Aladdin's cave of vintage instruments in Staten Island, New York. There among the old Gibsons was this top-of-the-range looking Ovation. I'd never really liked Ovations before, but I did the classic double take on it when I saw it had 8 strings. I played it and was amazed by the volume and tone coming off the thing. It filled the shop. I had been looking at 1916 Gibson K4s and the like but this really pressed my buttons. I left the shop with the 1921 A2 mandolin but couldn't stop thinking about the Ovation. When I got back to England I ordered one. When it arrived it was still in tune

You're able to accompany tunes on the mandocello or the bouzouki-guitar in a really inventive, non-guitaristic way. Are there any harmonic tricks that you employ that you can let us know about or is it all pure instinct?

I think being a bass player is the secret. I base my chord progressions over interesting bass-lines so it fills out the accompaniment more than strumming a chord sequence. Also there are two main shapes on any mandolin family instrument, for example [2nd fret G string, 2nd fret D string, 4th fret A string] and its minor version which take a lot of the thinking out of accompaniment. You have tenths between the G and A strings, which is an old trick of Oscar Peterson's and it's easy enough to adapt these shapes for flattened fifths, augmented chords, and so on.

Maart's closing comments contain some simple but valuable advice. Here are his two 'main shapes' which he uses as a kicking off point for accompaniments; they can be placed anywhere on the neck, on either the top three or (as shown) the bottom three strings. Think of them as the basis of more complex chords on the mandolin.

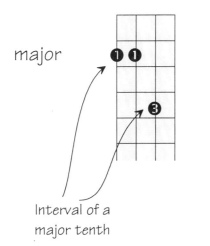

major

Interval of a
major tenth

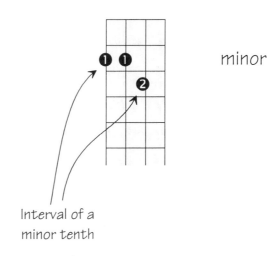

minor

Interval of a
minor tenth

Think of the interval of a tenth as the same as a third; really it's an octave and a third. Either way, it's a very important interval in music because it is the major/minor indicator.

The Chris Newman Interview

To many who have seen him in concert, Chris Newman is the definitive Celtic style guitarist. After cutting his teeth on jazz and bluegrass, aided in no small way by jazz legend Diz Disley, his early career was dominated by session work and as producer and musical director for more mainstream artists.

In the 80s he teamed up with Irish harpist Máire ní Chathasaigh, took a decision that from then he was going to play what *he* wanted to play, and set about mastering the subtleties of Irish music on both guitar and mandolin. He has since toured internationally with Máire, The Boys of the Lough and many other highly respected artists in the field. Although he thinks of himself primarily as a guitarist, his forays on the mandolin are guaranteed to leave *anybody* open-jawed....

Were you attracted to the mandolin for its own sake or was it simply an easy matter of adapting your guitar technique?

I was originally attracted to the mandolin as I thought it made a nice noise. It was also a relatively easy instrument to get to grips with - the left hand fingerings are obviously different and when I play mandolin, it always takes me a few minutes to get into 'fifth mode', so to speak. I do appreciate the fact that all the strings are tuned the same way though, unlike the guitar. It makes transposition a lot simpler.

What about your right hand? Do you find any major differences between your approach to the guitar and the mandolin?

My right hand technique is pretty much the same as the guitar. I use the same pick on both the guitar and mandolin - it's a Dunlop 1 mm nylon. I've used them for years - they never break, just gradually wear out until they're so small I'm obliged to buy a new one. I only ever use one pick at a time, and generally get about 2 years out of each one. Dunlop won't make a fortune out of me!

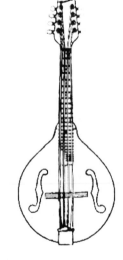

Have you found an 'ideal' instrument yet or are you on a constant search?

I think the nicest mandolin I've ever played is a Vanden - a terrific instrument. I have a Gibson A50 from the early fifties which is OK, and a big improvement on the Ibanez I used to have, but it doesn't excite me when I play it! My guitar, on the other hand, is an absolutely wonderful old Martin which gives me a huge thrill every time I take it out of the case and play an E major chord. What a sound - the A50 certainly isn't in that category. I'm not actively looking for another guitar (although I always have an eye open for something that might be better) but I would very much like a better mandolin.

Yes, well there are certainly a lot of fine instrument makers around at the moment, and I suppose to be fair to Gibson, the A50 was their 'cheap' model. But you obviously prefer Gibson style instruments for playing Celtic music. You don't think their sound is too 'North American' - too associated with bluegrass for the job?

Absolutely not - I don't really think of a 'North American'

sound as such - I just like the noise that flat-back mandolins make.

Many players have a strong preference for the sound of either oval or f-hole instruments. Do you?

No, I don't really have an opinion on this, but one thing I positively loathe is the sound of some instruments made to a so-called 'English' pattern by certain makers in this country! They really are the pits - I've even seen some with only 16 frets - you can't even hit a top A!

Have you experimented much with string gauges and action settings?

I've no idea what the gauges are...

Are you serious?

Seriously! I've been getting my guitar strings from Malcolm Newton [Newtone Strings] for some years, and about a year ago I realised the strings on the mando were, well, black is probably the best description. I called Malcolm and asked him to send me a few regular mando sets. They duly arrived and I put some on the A50 - instant improvement, although the gauges are unknown to me. I've never experimented with the action either - I suppose I should, but I never have.

Not necessarily. Some mandolins seem to just work from the start; I've never touched the action on mine either! Let's talk about Celtic music now; you've been immersed in it - mostly Irish - for quite a few years, what's your approach to decorating tunes?

I vary decoration, but within certain known stylistic boundaries. I don't learn decorations for individual tunes as there is no hard and fast way to do it - three, or thirty, different players will decorate things in different places, and they could all be quite correct. I wouldn't do a free for all either, but I'd put in the variations and ornaments within the style of the piece.

Yes, I think this notion of stylistic boundaries is interesting. I don't know whether you'd agree, but what I find overwhelming is when some players finally crack the way to do triplets and then completely overuse the technique to the extent that the melody becomes obscured?

I agree - there are far too many people who think they've cracked it when they figure out

how to do a triplet. The important thing is where you put it... there's no easier way to ruin a good Irish tune than to shove in triplets in completely the wrong place. A triplet is nothing more than an essential tool required to play the tunes properly - in the correct style. The same applies to cuts and rolls of course...

You've played for many years now with Irish harper Máire Ní Chathasaigh; I was wondering to what extent she's influenced your style?

Máire has been of enormous benefit to me in learning the correct styles, in much the same way that Diz Disley was all those years ago with swing jazz. I don't consider that I have an Irish style of playing - I like to think that I can play those tunes properly, but I try to play other styles just as accurately. My overall style is, I suppose, a complete mixture of everything I've ever done.

Tell us your thoughts on the thorny subject of pick direction. Forgetting decoration for a moment, when you're playing jigs are you a 'down-up-down, down-up-down man' or a 'down-up-down, up-down-up' man? I can see arguments for both approaches, although I have my own preference.

I'm very much a 'DUD, UDU' person - it gets awkward sometimes with triplets, but that's easily overcome by starting on an upstroke. There again, it depends where in the tune the triplet falls... in general I would always default to 'DUD, UDU'. It's also tricky when crosspicking, but like anything else, you get used to it with practice.

You mentioned jazz guitarist Diz Disley; it must have been a real luxury having Diz as mentor when you were younger, and I know improvising is certainly second nature to you on guitar. Do you find it as easy on mandolin, and do you find yourself tempted to jam round the melody when you're playing traditional tunes?

Working with Diz for so long was immensely helpful to me when I started out on the whole improvisation thing. I find it very easy on the guitar, but quite difficult on the mandolin. In fact, almost impossible! My problem is that I know where all the notes are on the guitar - I am completely comfortable anywhere on the fretboard in any position - simply because I've been at it for so long. The mandolin is entirely different for me - I can't instinctively mess around with a tune as the position of all the notes isn't second nature to me. I'd have to spend a lot longer becoming really familiar with the instrument before I could confidently zoom around all over the place. Every time I need to do a mandolin solo I do what I never do on the guitar - I work out what I want to play, learn it, record it and promptly forget it as I'll almost certainly never need to do it again!

One piece you're famous for is 'A Sor Point' - which you play as impressively on mandolin as you do on guitar. What gave you the idea of turning a piece by Fernando Sor into an 'Irish' jig?

I first heard the tune played by the absolutely incomparable Alexandre Lagoya and Ida Presti - the two greatest classical guitar players I've ever heard. What initially attracted me to the piece was not so much the technical brilliance, but the way in which they played together. I've yet to hear a finer example of duo ensemble playing in any style or genre. I listened to the piece over and over, and doing the conversion to a jig sort of evolved. I'd try to play along with the CD, but the speed was ferocious - I slowed it down a fair bit and it became a jig.

Surely it's much more technically demanding than your average jig?

Not really - there are far fewer ornaments and variations than on a 'proper' jig. It's fast, of course, but playing fast is not difficult - just a question of starting slowly and gradually building up the tempo. Long live the quartz metronome!

Are you the sort of person who practises scales and arpeggios or do you just play tunes?

I went through a phase a few years ago of practising scales and arpeggios on the guitar - never on the mandolin. I did it for a while but became bored so don't do it any more.

What about any set practice and warm-up routines?

I used to have a series of exercises, but I haven't done them for years. Funnily enough I find I play better if I've had a few days away - it's always great to go away on holiday without an instrument and then return to it after the break. I get a real kick out of taking it from the case and thinking "great - I can do this".

The Brian Taheny Interview

Now resident in Canada, multi-instrumentalist Brian Taheny is originally from Sligo in Ireland. A master of his native tradition, his strong, rhythmic style bears a deep awareness of the ornamentation and subtleties of Irish music. He is an aggressive player who knows how to put the essential 'lift' into a tune.

With whistle player Loretto Reid, he plays mandolin, guitar, banjo and fiddle with *The Reid/Taheny Band* and is also a busy session musician, recording engineer and producer.

I know traditional music is alive and well in pretty much all corners of Ireland but is it particularly thriving in Sligo?

Sligo has always been famous for fiddle and flute players, but there was a very wide generation gap between myself and other players. Other players in Sligo of my age at that time, the mid 70s, included virtuoso tin whistle player Loretto Reid - now my musical partner and wife - and fiddle player Maurice Lennon from Stockton's Wing. However, we were fortunate to play in regular sessions with many marvellous older musicians: flute players Josie McDermott, Packie Duigan, fiddle and flute duo Fred Finn and Peter Horan, and especially [fiddler] Joe O'Dowd who was an accomplished master of the Sligo style of playing, as well as being a wonderful man. Through these sessions I learned a lot from concentrated osmosis!

What about the mandolin in particular? It's obviously not as widely played as the fiddle or pipes, but does its history in Irish music go back as far as those instruments?

No, I don't have a lot of information on its history, but the first mandolin players I would have known in the Irish tradition were the great Barney McKenna of the Dubliners and Johnny Moynihan, Andy Irvine and Terry Woods of Sweeney's Men - all players from the 1960s on. So it would appear to me that the mandolin, before this time, would not have competed with the louder session instruments and it was with the advent of the folk boom - folk clubs and so on - and the quieter vocal groups that the mandolin had a chance to become a serious lead and backing instrument.

Tell me about how you got into it. Were there any particular musicians when you were young who turned you onto the mandolin?

My mother was bugging me and wanting to hear me play the mandolin "just like Barney!" I had been playing the guitar for about a year and was getting into Irish traditional music from listening to early Horslips, I decided that the mandolin seemed a logical step, so I bought my first instrument - an EKO electric mandolin, along with a wah-wah pedal! It became obvious pretty soon that one needed to have unnaturally small and strong fingers to play on this particular plank of wood - but it was cheap! So I progressed to a decent Japanese A style copy with f-holes and now I could join in sessions locally.

Although I didn't know or pass heed of it beforehand, my Dad, Dermot, had been a violin player in cafe orchestras during the 40s and 50s, and showed me how to read music slowly. I purchased O'Neill's *1001 Gems* and asked the players at the sessions the tune names whenever I heard one that took my fancy, then I would slowly practise a tune or two that week so I could play along with it at the next week's session, slowly building up a repertoire and adding techniques and so on. I purchased a book on bluegrass mandolin, the only tutor I could find on the instrument and went through it picking up on double stops, alternate picking and things, and some of these techniques found their way into my playing.

Having heard you play at very close range, I must say I was struck by what a powerful plectrum technique you have. I don't think I've heard anyone play with more attack. I know you're a fine guitarist and fiddler as well, but would I be right in thinking this derives from a banjo technique?

I think it comes from playing in big sessions - maybe four or five flutes, two or three fiddles, tin whistles, accordions and maybe a banjo, and trying to compete in volume - no easy task!!! I didn't own a banjo until I had played mandolin and bouzouki for three or four years, so it was more transferring my techniques to the banjo and adapting them to the sound of the instrument.

Still on the right hand: do you find any major differences between your approach to the guitar and the mandolin?

After getting a mandolin, the big shock was just how different an instrument it was from the guitar. I had never flat-picked tunes on the guitar, so now I had to learn tunes and play a lot louder and faster - it was a bit like being thrown in at the deep end! But the energy at sessions fascinated me and although I had a hard time differentiating one tune from another, I stuck at it and practised as much as I could. Sessions of three hours' music or more will improve your right hand no end, or else give you a bad dose of tendonitus and frustration! It taught me to anchor my right hand well and use as little movement as possible in my wrist to keep the music flowing over long periods of time.

Yes, I think this goal of minimal movement with maximum effect is an important one for all musicians. If you watch any good instrumentalist in any musical genre you'll probably be surprised at how little they move their fingers to achieve what they do. It's all to do with efficiency of movement, and perhaps following on from that, this would be a good point to ask you about how you approach pick direction...

Well here's a very hard one to answer as it's very difficult to analyse one's own pick directions. I can tell you that I tend to play a lot more down strokes than up. For triplets, I tend to play mostly 'down-up-down', but I also find that sometimes I will play 'up-down-up'. The important thing in the tune is the feel, so the pick direction has to adjust to keep things fluid.

When learning a tune, I concentrate on the melody, phrasing and ornamentation. Often decorations can appear as I'm practising. It's also important in Irish music to vary the phrasing and ornamentation as often as possible during the repeats of the tune. To allow this to happen spontaneously takes a lot of practice. I remember diligently practising triplets for a year before I'd accomplished playing them to my liking, then there's always all the other forms of ornaments. To all practising Celtic mandolinists out there, keep at it, play to the best of your ability and keep pushing yourself. Make tapes of your playing and play along to yourself, changing things about. It really does pay off... eventually!

I'm really interested to learn more about how you approach decoration. Does your style derive, for example, from the Sligo fiddle style or is it just pure 'Taheny'?

Yes, a certain amount of influence would have come from the Sligo regional fiddle style, but strangely enough the instrument that influenced me the most in my approach to the mandolin was the Uilleann Pipes. The big piping tunes are very compatible on stringed instruments and always present a challenge, with techniques such as rolls, triplets and crans: the three essentials in Irish traditional music. I was also performing in bands and sessions with Loretto Reid, so her playing techniques, especially slides, bends and phrasings influenced my playing a lot. Later on when P J Hernon the Galway-spirited accordion player moved to Sligo, his style was also an influence.

Tell me now about the instrument you play.

I play a small scale flat-back mandolin, made by A Galiano - which apparently was made in New York around the early 1920s. I had the fingerboard modified with a slight radius. It has a woody tone, but it has its limitations: it's particularly susceptible to tuning problems and has low volume.

I found my ideal mandolin about two years ago when I walked into a local guitar shop and played on a Gibson F4 oval hole from about 1918. Unfortunately, I didn't, and still don't, have the money to purchase this wonderful box, but had to console myself by monthly stops at the shop to play just a few more tunes on it, until one day it was gone. For me this instrument had everything - unparalleled tone and volume, a remarkable fingerboard with ample room to manoeuvre, a perfect left hand grip on the chunky neck and the most beautiful inlay work and appearance of any instrument I've ever seen - Ah! Some day!

In the meantime, I'm working with Tom Robinson Music of Forest, Ontario and master luthier Don Carter to develop a 10 string cittern to my personal requirements and specification. If all goes well, who knows, we may be tempted to come up with the ideal carved top and back Celtic mandolin. Don has been building top notch f-hole mandolins and arch top guitars for many years now and we're looking forward to a new line of players' stringed Celtic instruments to come onto the market here shortly.

What's your preferred set-up on a mandolin?

I use Dr Thomastick flat-wound strings for their tone and long life. My pick is generally medium gauge plastic - never nylon. At present I'm using Dunlop Tortex 0.5mm, they have enough flexibility for triplets without excessive 'pick-clicks'. I hold my pick very firmly between my thumb and first two fingers with the tip just showing out. My mandolin string action is medium to low.

You've lived in North America for some time now. Has your style changed at all since you've mixed with Canadian and American players?

I wouldn't say my style has changed much but I have more versatility from meeting and jamming with other players of the various North American styles of music. This more undiluted exposure has widened my repertoire and adaptation to playing in different traditional situations. It's opened my choices and allowed me a more educated approach to

The Gary Peterson Interview

The mandolin may not be the most obvious instrument to take up when you come from a place bursting at the seams with fine fiddlers, but Shetlander Gary Peterson has carved an enviable reputation through his mastery of not only local, but Scottish and Irish styles. His overall plectrum control and in particular his crisp execution of triplets are remarkable. His band, Hom Bru, make all too rare trips across the water, but the recordings are worth seeking out, or better still, take a trip to Shetland...

Are you a native Shetlander?

Yes.

I ask because I'm intrigued that you were attracted to take up the mandolin in a place where the fiddle is king and the inspiration to learn it must be overwhelming.

Well the mandolin rather runs in the family, my father plays it and my grandfather played it.

Incidentally, do you class Shetland as a Celtic tradition, because I know there's a strong Scandinavian influence on the culture there?

It's a halfway house really; a lot of the older tunes do have a strong Scandinavian influence, but much of the contemporary Shetland music is more Celtic sounding nowadays, with a Scottish, even Irish influence.

So did you get formal lessons from your father and grandfather?

No, I just taught myself. But because the mandolin's lying there in the house you want to try it. I think my father showed me the scales, but that's about all.

Is there a mandolin scene that runs parallel to the fiddle scene on Shetland?

Yes, but there are certainly not as many players. I think the mandolin scene grew up because for a lot of Shetlanders in the 50s and 60s the main employment was being away at sea, and I suppose the mandolin's a fine size of thing to take on board.

Of course it's tuned the same as a fiddle, and I suppose it was a more robust instrument for those conditions.

That's right.

Do you play fiddle as well?

No. I started on mandolin and I can do the left hand on the fiddle, obviously, but I find the bowing difficult.

Was it exclusively Shetland music that you grew up with or did you play other styles as well?

Just about every kind of music! I used to play a lot of Greek and Italian tunes - with lots of tremolo - I think that's maybe helped me to develop the style I have of playing traditional tunes because it's more or less short bursts of tremolo I'm using.

It was this right hand technique that really impressed me when I first heard you - how crisp your triplets were, in fact all the decorative tricks you use. Do you put that down to learning Italian style?

Well, I think it's helped a lot. You see most traditional players - most Irish players, that is - use triplets but I think I'm actually doing five notes. At first, I hadn't noticed I was doing anything different from other players, but I think it was Dick Gaughan who actually said to me "Do you realise you're doing five?"

And presumably you didn't realise?

Well, I'm just using short bursts of tremolo, you see. I remember a Scottish drummer I met telling me that I placed my 'triplets' at the same time as he would have done a roll on the drums... in certain tunes.

Is this something you've consciously worked on? Not just where to place triplets but other types of decoration?

No, I don't consciously work on anything. I hear a tune and just play it the way I feel. The choice of plectrum is important, though; I use a Jim Dunlop .73mm nylon, asymmetrical. I use the pointed end. It used to be a .60mm but I've gone on to the .73mm this last couple of years; it's better for the triplets and gives a better tone, although I still use the .60mm on a tenor banjo.

I use an asymmetrically shaped plectrum as well, but play mostly on one of the rounded corners. For me, it gives a thicker tone, but I imagine the slightly more brilliant sound you get from the pointed end is very important for your style.

Yes. In fact, I was amazed when I found that a lot of bluegrass players use the rounded corner. I vary tone by changing the distance I play from the bridge.

Are you careful to choose tunes that are mandolinistic? After all most traditional tunes were written for fiddle or pipes, and the techniques of playing those instruments don't necessarily transfer well to mandolin.

I'll more or less have a stab at anything.

I thought you'd say that! You can play the mandolin in a style that is very reminiscent of highland pipe decorations. I've heard Alasdair Fraser do similar things on the fiddle, where a 'snap' onto a note is not

simply coming from the next higher note in the scale, but a wider interval, a fourth or a fifth above.

That's the sort of thing I do, but it started unconsciously because I've listened to a lot of pipe music. I like a lot of the pipe tunes; they've got a great swing to them. So I do similar grace notes.

What about slow airs? How do you approach them?

We have two mandolin players in the band [Hom Bru] and we use tremolo a lot, playing in harmony. I always say that the mandolin is a fast instrument - and on the slow stuff you've got to go even faster!

Finally, what's your mandolin?

It's a Kentucky F5. I'm very happy with it; I picked it up in a shop in Lerwick and it just seemed perfect - the feel and everything. Sometimes things just feel right. I used to use an old round-back that my father and grandfather had used. My grandfather also played at weddings with a banjo-mandolin; it had the volume before PA systems were around! But it doesn't figure in what I do now.

The Simon Mayor Interview

As this tome neared completion, the author would lay awake at night knowing there was a missing ingredient. It was as important as the salt in the fruit salad, the custard on the lamb chop, but was yet to be discovered.

Then, as the wind howled and the slates rattled, and the moon hid behind heavy clouds, a blinding light appeared, and he decided to allow himself to be subjected to the rigours of interview just as he had subjected others. And even discovered some things he didn't know about himself...

Is the mandolin your first instrument?

No. I got a ukulele when I was about eight; I'd been going mad for a guitar but I don't think my parents wanted to risk any sizeable amount of money. Ukes were cheap and playable, and weren't too loud. I think they're a great idea for anyone just wanting to find out if they've got any aptitude for a fretted instrument. They bought me a guitar a couple of years later for ten shillings - a mint! My Dad was very musical in an untrained sort of way and he taught me to play by ear, even though he didn't play any stringed instrument himself. He used to sit by the radio and just write a tune down in tonic sol-fa as somebody was singing it, then he'd get me to play it on the guitar, singing the tonic sol-fa and getting me to copy. It's ingrained now, I still think of all tunes in tonic sol-fa.

Did you get any formal lessons as well?

No. Lessons were not on the financial agenda! I had Bert Weedon's 'Play In A Day' guitar tutor and worked my way through it like an awful lot of people of my vintage. I think progress would have been quicker if I'd have had a teacher, but you hear of so many people being put off by formal lessons that it's very important to find one who's sympathetic. I think the most important role for a teacher, whether it's someone acting formally or just as an informal mentor, is to inspire. Once someone is sufficiently inspired, they'll learn with or without lessons.

When did the mandolin come along?

I was about seventeen and got into the fiddle. I realised the mandolin was tuned the same, so it was an obvious instrument to play given that I'd learned plectrum guitar.

So was there anyone in particular who turned you on to it?

My cousin, who was a fine guitarist, had a mandolin but it was more of a curio that hung on the wall. He didn't play it too much. Then I heard 'Rags, Reels and Airs', Dave Swarbrick's old recording with Martin Carthy and Diz Disley. I'd already been getting into fiddle players, listening to people like Aly Bain and Barry Dransfield, but Swarbrick was doing just as much on the mandolin as the fiddle. Then about the same time I heard some classical mandolin music: Hugo D'Alton playing some Beethoven, and the Ochi recordings of the Vivaldi concertos, and I found myself pretty quickly absorbed by the whole mandolin thing. I started learning lots of traditional tunes, all the things on 'Rags, Reels and Airs'. I didn't know or care whether they were Scottish, Irish, English or whatever, I just played them as fast as I could. You know what's important when you're young!

Isn't speed important now?

Well, it's wonderful to hear some reels played really fast, provided the speed doesn't get in the way of the musicality. It's not good hearing someone playing beyond their technique just because they think it's important to play fast. If you listen to someone like Martin Hayes on the fiddle, he plays much more steadily than most people, although I've no doubt he could tear along if he wanted to. But the way he interprets a tune is every bit as valid as a speed merchant.

The way you execute a tune is the most important thing, the way you make your instrument talk - whatever instrument - and that's down to having total control over your digits, and total co-ordination. Obviously everybody is going to have their own speed 'ceiling'.

Do you have your mandolin set up fast?

I certainly have a lower action than a bluegrass player would want, but I do use heavy strings, .040 to .011. It's always a compromise between playability and tone; a high action and heavy strings will give you a wonderful sound but make it impossible to play. Everybody has to find their own ideal set-up. For beginners it probably makes sense to go for playability over tone, but your fingers do get stronger over the years.

How do you know that?

Well, from my own experience. I used to play a Japanese round-back when I first got into classical music. It was extremely easy to

play, apart from the back wobbling about of course. It had a short scale, low action, not a bad sound for a factory instrument. I remember trying some Gibsons (which I couldn't afford) and even the shortish scale A models seemed really stiff in comparison. Eventually I bought the mandolin I still use today, Mike Vanden's Model F. It's long scale and I now put heavy strings on it, but it doesn't seem a problem, so my fingers must have got stronger I suppose.

Or your technique's improved?

Well, yes, that has something to do with it as well. A lot of people make it difficult for themselves by doing things in an inefficient way, and over the years you learn to do things more effectively, or at least you should. I'm always harping on about maximum effect with minimum effort; it's a good motto for anything really, not just playing an instrument.

Can you tell me more about your mandolin?

I bought it from a dealer, not from the maker, although I later contacted Mike Vanden and asked for a mandola and mandocello. These other two instruments are quite striking, blown-up F5 mandolins with scrolls and points. My mandolin is really his cheap model: teardrop shape, but otherwise built like an F5 with f-holes and bass bar. He once told me that it was an experiment to see if he could get the best possible sound the cheapest possible way. It's now the only style he wants to make. I was getting a bit dissatisfied with the round-back; it was only a factory model I suppose, but at the same time I hadn't been attracted to Gibsons because they didn't have the sustain I was looking for. My mandolin had sustain in abundance, even when it was new, as well as a wonderful thick tone. I scarcely put it down for the first 48 hours I had it. I think Gibson had a lot of good ideas, and I have a strong preference for their carved top and back, shallow body design, but it's taken modern luthiers to realise the potential of it all. There are many good individual makers around nowadays, I've seen Gilchrists and Nuggets that have really impressed me. The craft has undoubtedly taken off these last ten or twenty years.

Was changing from the round-back difficult?

Yes, both physically and psychologically. Suddenly I had the long scale to contend with, but I was determined to get used to it as it sounded so much better. It seems crazy now as round-backs feel so cramped whenever I play one. Also, while I knew the Vanden sounded fantastic for the traditional music, all the classical mandolin I had ever heard had been on round-backs and I sort of assumed it wouldn't be suitable for the job. I now know that's not the case, but people would come up to me and say "Oh, you're playing a bluegrass instrument." Well, all I knew was that I had a mandolin that was doing what I wanted a mandolin to do. The message seems a lot clearer now: never be scared to trust your own ears, don't look at the name on the top, don't necessarily think that an expensive instrument is going to be the best for you, just trust your own ears.

Yes, Chris Newman makes a similar point in his interview. I think a lot of people aren't aware that the carved design actually predates bluegrass; Gibson originally made these instruments for the whole mandolin orchestra craze in the States. Incidentally, do you have a preference for oval or f-hole instruments?

I have a strong preference for f-holes. They go 'piiiiiiiiiiiiiing' whereas oval-holes go 'plop'. But that could be because I've played an f-hole mandolin for many years and I suppose my playing style will have developed accordingly.

Tell me about the plectrum you use

An ordinary, asymmetrical, plastic, medium gauge, something about .75mm. I have no brand preference. Someone once gave me a tortoiseshell one - old stock of course as it's illegal these days - and I'm relieved to say I'm not too keen, which means I won't even be tempted to use it. I'm not much fond of nylon either, although a lot of people get a great sound with nylon picks. Golden Gates, the really thick, rounded ones, seem to work well for some people, but I find I can't vary the tone sufficiently with them, and they're

a little inflexible for triplets. With a medium gauge you can still produce a brilliance with the pointed end, or you can use one of the rounded corners, angled slightly as it crosses the strings, to thicken the tone. I sometimes even swivel it round in my hand in the middle of a piece to use a different corner. Maybe this is all a bit idiosyncratic but it does work for me.

Do you have any practice routines?

No, I never have had. I've always played a lot, but it's always been for pleasure rather than a sense of duty. Practising scales and arpeggios will help, there's no doubt, but I think the fastest way to improve is playing as much as possible with other people. I started playing for dances years ago with Brian Willcocks, a wonderful accordion player with a huge repertoire of Celtic tunes. He had about fifteen years more experience than me, and still has, come to think of it! He was adamant we shouldn't use any printed music, but I knew hardly any of his tunes. It didn't matter though, because we were playing for dancing and people were only interested in the rhythm. The melodies found their way into my head eventually. I'm sure nobody bothered about any wrong notes I played; they probably never even noticed them because all they were listening to was the rhythm. All I knew was that I could have a go in total safety because I knew the sound wasn't going to fall apart. This led to my experimenting with improvisation, again in total safety because the accordion was like the musical rock of ages, and people weren't listening to you as critically as they would at a jazz club for example. Eventually you find you can do these things It's all down to playing with others.

Do you still play for dances?

Yes, and I still find it as valuable as ever. I also find it relaxing in a way that doing a formal concert isn't. I think the social thing is the basis of all music, whether it's a few friends meeting in somebody's kitchen or a pub session, or playing for a dance.

More CDs, Books and Videos

The Mandolin Album
CDACS 012

'Uplifting and a joy' DAILY TELEGRAPH
'Sheer joy' FOLK ROOTS

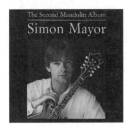

The Second Mandolin Album
CDACS014

'Simply a masterpiece'
TOWER RECORDS MAGAZINE
'Refreshing and uplifting' VOX

Winter with Mandolins
CDACS 015

Recording of the Week BBC WORLD SERVICE
'The most beautiful bell-like mandolin sound I have ever heard, the sound simply sparkles.'
THE LIVING TRADITION

The English Mandolin
CDACS025

'A work of epic proportions touched with a regal quality.' ROCK 'N' REEL

The New Mandolin
(Tune Book)
ISBN 0-9522776-0-3

21 original tunes by Simon Mayor taken from across the first three mandolin albums transcribed in both conventional music and tablature, with chords, fingerings, playing advice and amusing anecdotes.

The Mandolin Tutor - Book / CD
ISBN 0-9522776-1-1 / CDACS028

A detailed course for those starting to play the mandolin, covering everything from tuning, right and left hand techniques, reading music and tablature, chords, tremolo, scales, tunes, exercises and simple duets to advice on choosing and maintaining an instrument.

'Way, way better than anything of this sort that I've seen' - FOLK ROOTS

Mandolin Essentials - Teaching Video
VTACS 031

Tips, tunes and technique for the early stages of mandolin playing

In an informal and encouraging approach, Simon Mayor gets you playing five easy tunes from a variety of musical idioms.

More From Simon Mayor

If you would like up-to-date news of books, recordings and concerts by
Simon Mayor drop a line to Acoustics. You can use the form below
(feel free to photocopy it but please don't copy other pages).

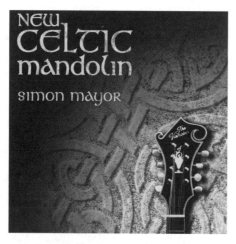

*Mrs Murray of Abercarney, Waynesboro, Carolan's
Frolics, Little Molly-O, Dance of the Water Boatmen,
Huish The Cat, Dérobée de Guingamp / Eliz Iza,
Farewell to the Shore / Ymdaith Gwyr Dyfnaint, Aye La
Le Lo, Niel Gow's Lament for Abercarney, Mount and Go,
The Butterfly, The Wasp Reel, Teetotaller's Fancy, The
Dark and Slender Boy*

New Celtic Mandolin CD

with Beryl Marriott, Frank Kilkelly, Hilary James

'In Mayor's hands, the mandolin sings, whether it be in
the virtuosic uptempo numbers or the achingly beautiful
slow airs… extraordinary tenderness, as on Little
Molly-O and Niel Gow's Lament for Abercarney. A
brilliant album! A real ear-opener!'

Delyth Jenkins, Taplas magazine (Wales)

'What comes across here is the melody, and there are
some lovely ones in the 53 minutes of this recording.'

Alex Monaghan, Living Tradition

' … dazzling display of the instrument's many voices…
virtuoso musician Simon Mayor is bestowed with such a
mastery that each piece is a real moment of joy. Whether
it be from Ireland, Scotland, New England or Brittany the
instrument sustains an incredible fluency and an
incredible sense of swing.'

Alain Hermanstadt, Trad magazine (France)

New Celtic Mandolin - Teaching Video

Waynesboro
Dance of the Water Boatmen
The Butterfly
The Dark and Slender Boy
The Athol Highlanders

A chance to see Simon Mayor
playing some of the music from this
book. With a clear, detailed,
play-as-you-learn approach he
guides you through five of the most
popular tunes. *(53 mins)*

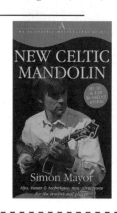

Please keep me informed of future books, recordings and concerts by Simon Mayor

Name .... Address ....
....
.... Postcode ....

What style of music do you like/play?   Celtic/Folk ☐   Classical ☐   Jazz ☐
                                         Country / Bluegrass ☐   Pop ☐   Other ....

Do you play any other instruments? If yes which one/s? ....

ACOUSTICS

PO Box 350, Reading RG6 7DQ, Berks, England
Tel: 0118 926 8615   ◆   Fax: 0118 935 3216
email: AcousticsRecords@compuserve.com
http://ourworld.compuserve.com/homepages/AcousticsRecords

NCMB